FIRE MOUNTAIN

Written by
GLEN DOWNEY

Illustrated by
LIAM THURSTON

This story is set in ancient Roman times, in towns close to Mount Vesuvius in Italy. Each chapter ends with a non-fiction page that gives more information about real people's lives, plus facts linked to the events at that time.

OXFORD
UNIVERSITY PRESS

CATO

PLINY THE ELDER

PLINY THE YOUNGER

POMPONIANUS

REAL PEOPLE IN HISTORY

PLINY THE ELDER (AD/CE **23-79**): He was a commander of the Roman navy and a scientist who studied nature.

PLINY THE YOUNGER (AD/CE **62-113**): Pliny the Elder's nephew. He was only 17 years old at the time of the eruption.

POMPONIANUS (dates unknown): A friend of Pliny the Elder.

FICTIONAL CHARACTERS

CATO: A 10-year-old slave boy from the city of Pompeii.

MINERVA: Cato's mother.

STEPHANUS: The slave master of Cato and Minerva.

DIANA: A 12-year-old slave girl from Pompeii who becomes Cato's friend.

CATO

MINERVA

STEPHANUS

DIANA

Contents

THOUSANDS FLEE SUMATRA VOLCANO
BBC News, 13 April 2005

VOLCANO ERUPTS, COVERS COLOMBIA IN ASH
Associated Press, 24 November 2005

ERUPTIONS PUT ALASKANS ON VOLCANO ALERT
Associated Press, 15 January 2006

Today, we can read and hear news about volcanic activities as soon as they happen in any part of the world. We can also get information and images of volcanic eruptions over the Internet.

The letters BCE stand for 'Before Common Era'. The years before the Common Era are counted backwards, so the greater the number, the longer ago it was. For example, 89 BCE is further in the past than 23 BCE.

TIMELINE

600 BC/BCE »	89 BC/BCE »	AD/CE 23 »	AD/CE 62 »
The town of Pompeii, located southeast of Naples, is founded.	Pompeii becomes an important port for goods going to Rome or southern Italy.	Pliny the Elder is born in Como, Italy.	Pliny's nephew, Pliny the Younger, is born. In this year, a series of earthquakes rocks Pompeii, damaging several buildings.

We know how volcanoes work. Deep under the Earth's crust is molten (melted) rock called magma. As magma cools, it gives off gases and builds up pressure. When the pressure becomes too great, the magma and its gases break through a weak spot in a mountain, and a volcanic eruption takes place.

Volcanic eruptions can give off poisonous gases and spew out hot, molten rocks. They can also cause earthquakes and landslides.

Cross-section of a volcano

Lava flow

Ruins of Pompeii

On 24 August in AD/CE 79, a huge volcanic eruption occurred in the beautiful Bay of Naples in Italy. The volcano was Vesuvius, and the eruption was the first in history to be recorded in detail. This story is about Vesuvius and what happened when this fire mountain roared!

This story is set in an actual time in history, although some of the events are fictional. Real events during this period are shown on the timeline below.

AD/CE 79 >>	AD/CE 79 >>	AD/CE 113 >>	AD/CE 1738 >>	AD/CE 1748 >>
On 24 August, Mount Vesuvius erupts, burying Pompeii, Herculaneum and other surrounding towns.	On 26 August, Pliny the Elder is found dead on the beach at Stabiae.	Pliny the Younger dies.	Archaeologists discover the ancient city of Herculaneum.	Archaeologists discover the ancient city of Pompeii.

8

THE MOUNTAIN RUMBLES.

CATO!

CATO! WHAT'S WRONG?

I THINK I'VE TWISTED MY ANKLE. IT HURTS!

A MYSTERIOUS DARK CLOUD RISES UP INTO THE SKY.

The ruins of Pompeii

POMPEII AND VESUVIUS

Pompeii was an ancient Roman colony and an important city for trade. It was known for its wines and perfumes. Many wealthy Romans spent their holidays there.

Close to the city of Pompeii stood Mount Vesuvius, a volcano. This area was often jolted by large earthquakes.

A bad earthquake hit Pompeii in AD/CE 62, damaging several buildings. In AD/CE 79, a disastrous eruption occurred. It buried the towns of Herculaneum and Pompeii.

ITALY

Pompeii

Many buildings were destroyed.

THE PEOPLE ARE SO TERRIFIED THAT THEY DON'T EVEN FEEL THE PEOPLE THEY ARE STEPPING ON.

CATO TRIES TO GET ON HIS FEET.

I MUST FIND MY MOTHER ... WHILE THERE'S STILL TIME!

SLAVERY

Roman noble attended by many slaves

Many wealthy citizens in ancient Rome owned slaves. Slaves were required to do whatever tasks their masters gave them. Slaves who worked at a fullery, for instance, spent their days cleaning and folding the clothes that were brought there. If a slave ever tried to escape from his or her master, the penalty could be physical punishment or even worse!

Some slaves were trained to be gladiators. Gladiators fought against one another or against animals to entertain Roman citizens. Slaves did not always remain slaves for the rest of their lives. If they earned and saved enough money, they could buy their way out of slavery and become free.

Gladiators

21

Chapter 3: A Daring Escape

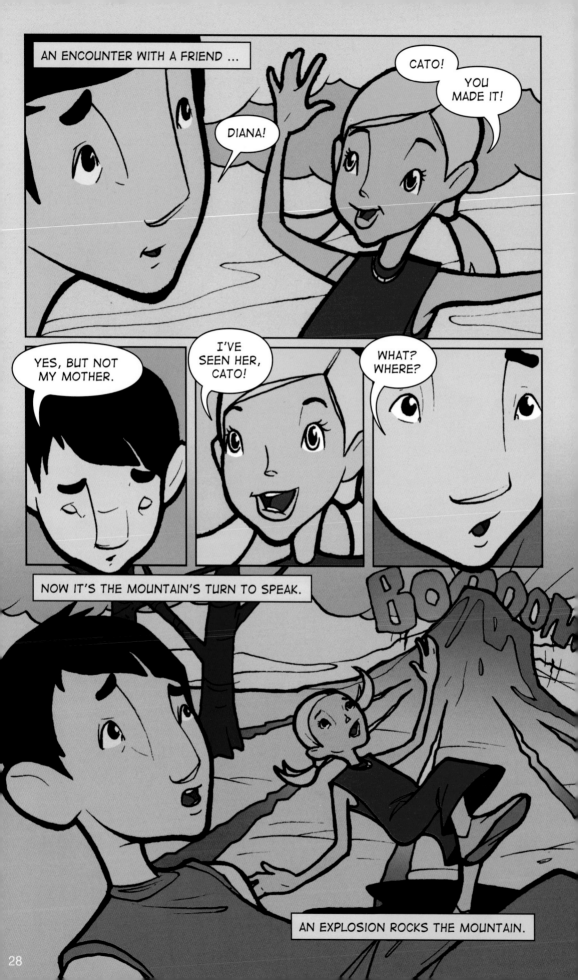

HERCULANEUM

Herculaneum was an ancient Roman town that was smaller but wealthier than Pompeii. It was located to the north and west of Pompeii, and to the west of Vesuvius.

When the mountain began to rumble at 1 p.m. on 24 August, many citizens of Herculaneum went down to the beach. They hoped to be rescued or to take shelter in the boathouses.

The next eruption occurred on the morning of 25 August. It took only four minutes for the hot ashes to reach Herculaneum and bury the people on the shore.

Some of the remains of the residents of Herculaneum were not discovered until 1982, more than 1,900 years after the eruption.

Plaster cast of a man who died at Herculaneum

PLINY
THE ELDER

Pliny the Elder was a scientist and a commander in the Roman navy. When he heard about the eruption of Vesuvius, he set out to help. His ship could not land at Pompeii, which had been hit by the eruption, so he chose the port of Stabiae. Then Stabiae was also hit. Pliny the Elder, like many others, died on the shore at Stabiae.

Pliny's nephew, Pliny the Younger, recorded the eruption of Vesuvius and his uncle's brave actions.

... Now came the dust, though still thinly. I looked back: a dense cloud loomed behind us, following us like a flood poured across the land.
... We had scarcely sat down when a darkness came that was not like a moonless or cloudy night, but more like the black of closed and unlighted rooms. You could hear women lamenting, children crying, men shouting.
... It grew lighter, though that seemed not a return of day, but a sign that the fire was approaching. The fire itself actually stopped some distance away, but darkness and ashes came again, a great weight of them ...

Without the young Pliny's letters, we would know very little about what happened that day.

THE SURGE CLOUD HAS NEARLY RUN OUT OF ENERGY...

... BUT ITS TOXIC FUMES ARE STILL POWERFUL.

Mount St. Helens

FAMOUS VOLCANOES

The eruption of Vesuvius in AD/CE 79 made it one of the world's most famous volcanoes. Here are some others:

- **World's biggest volcano**: Mauna Loa in Hawaii. Also the biggest mountain on Earth, Mauna Loa is 17 km high from its base on the sea floor. It covers an area of 5,200 square km and has a volume of 80,000 cubic km!

- **Longest-lasting eruption**: It's still going on! Mount Kilauea in Hawaii has been erupting since 1983. That's 23 years and counting!

- **Most powerful eruption in history**: Mount Tambora in Indonesia in 1815. This eruption threw so much dust into the air that world temperatures were lowered by 3 degrees Celsius. It was the deadliest volcanic eruption ever, killing 92,000 people.

- **Largest volcanic landslide**: Mount St. Helens, Washington, USA. The eruption in 1980 triggered a landslide that measured 58 square km in area. About 2.8 billion cubic metres of rock debris rushed down the mountainside at 250 km/h.

WHAT IT

Plaster casts of people killed in the eruptions of Vesuvius

For many centuries, Pompeii and Herculaneum were forgotten. Then, as archaeologists began to dig in the 16th century, they discovered these cities that were buried so many years ago.

WAS LIKE

The eruption happened so quickly that people were killed as they were going about their normal lives. Herculaneum was destroyed by burning ash and toxic gas. A steady rain of ash and rock fell over Pompeii and covered the city, killing thousands of people.

The hot ash that had buried the bodies turned into solid rock. As the bodies decomposed, they left holes in the rock. Archaeologists have filled these holes with plaster and created casts of people and animals killed that day. They have also dug out streets and buildings, as well as markets, temples, public baths and gardens.

Vesuvius has erupted dozens of times since AD/CE 79. It could strike again at any moment. This is worrying because thousands of people live and work near the mountain today.

Ruins of Pompeii

INDEX

GLOSSARY

ancient – very old

archaeologist – a person who studies old civilisations by digging for the remains of their cities and buildings

decomposed – decayed or rotten

eruption – when a volcano shoots out hot lava and ash

gladiator – a man who fought for public entertainment in ancient Rome

lament – express sorrow about something

landslide – a mass of rocks and mud sliding down a hillside

poisonous – harmful to a living thing

pressure – the force of something pressing (see page 5)

punishment – something that is done to you because you have done wrong

toxic fumes – harmful, maybe deadly, gas

tremor – a shaking or trembling movement

volcanic ashes – hot ash from the opening at the top of a volcano